Scholastic Transition Program

Student Workbook

LEVEL B

Illustration Credits

Rosekrans Hoffman pages 5, 6, 10,
Christine Joy Pratt pages 14, 15, 19, 20. 22
Ruth Linstromberg pages 24, 25, 26, 31, 32
Bart Rivers pages 34, 35, 36, 39, 40, 41, 42
Cover art: © Maya Brooks

Julie Durrell pages 45, 46, 49, 50, 51, 52
Hatley Mason pages 55, 56, 61, 62
Ann Iosa pages 65, 66, 71, 72,
Slug Signorino pages 75, 76, 80, 81, 82
Tint art by Vincent Jeffrey

Copyright © 1998 Scholastic Inc. All rights reserved.
Published by Scholastic Inc.
Printed in the U.S.A.
ISBN 0-590-45595-8

12 11 10 9 8 7 6 5 4   8 9/0   40

Table of Contents

Name _____ **Date** _____

Nature Words

Story Words

stone a small piece of rock

pebble a small, round stone

frog a small green or brown animal with webbed feet and long back legs

creature a living being, human or animal

alligator a large reptile with strong jaws and very sharp teeth

Everyday Words

grass a green plant with long, thin leaves

bird a creature with two legs, wings, feathers, and a beak

weed a useless plant that grows where it is not wanted

moon the body that moves around Earth once a month

pool a small area of still water

A Fill in the blanks with words from the boxes.

1. a useless plant   _ _ _ _

2. a living being   _ _ _ _ _ _ _ _

3. a small animal with webbed feet   _ _ _ _

4. a small, round stone   _ _ _ _ _ _

5. a small piece of rock   _ _ _ _ _

B Use a word from the boxes to finish each sentence.

1. I like to swim in a warm _____ of water.

2. The nest was made by a red _____.

3. The night sky was lit up by the _____.

4. At the swamp we saw a big, scaly _____.

5. I use a lawn mower to cut the _____.

In the book find three other words that are about nature. Write them in your Journal.

✔ Use for Grading

Name _____ **Date** _____

My Extraordinary Trip

A Read the conversation below. Find five words that look like Spanish words. Circle them.

Rosa: Did you go to an island last summer?

Doug: Yes. My parents and I went to Aruba.

Rosa: Was it an ordinary trip?

Doug: Not at all. It was extraordinary! There was an enormous storm!

Rosa: Was anything harmed?

Doug: A big monument fell down. But we were safe.

B Write the circled words next to the correct definitions below.

1. very unusual, remarkable _____

2. very large _____

3. a land area surrounded by water _____

4. usual, not special _____

5. something built to remember a person or event _____

Partners Find more words in the story that are similar to Spanish words.

Name _____   **Date** _____

Long o (o-e, oe)

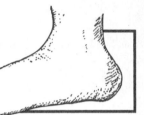

The letters *o-e* and *oe* can stand for the vowel sound you hear in *stone* and *toe*.

A Read each of the following words aloud. Listen for the long vowel sound. Then write each word under "Long *o* Spelled *o-e*" or "Long *o* Spelled *oe*."

rode	drove	potatoes	home
toe	dove	hoe	stone

Long *o* Spelled *o–e*	Long *o* Spelled *oe*
_____	_____
_____	_____
_____	_____
_____	_____
_____	_____

B Read each sentence. Fill in the blank with one of the words from above. Then circle the letters in each word that stand for the long *o* sound.

1. She likes to eat meat with _____ .

2. The car _____ down the road.

3. After school, we all walked _____ .

4. Someone stepped on my _____ .

5. The window was broken by a large _____ .

As you read the book, look for more words with long *o* spelled *o-e* and *oe*. Write the words in your Journal.

✔ Use for Grading

Name _____ **Date** _____

GET READY TO WRITE!

Choose an animal. Use the chart to help you organize your informative paragraph.

Remember
The main idea of the paragraph should be supported by several details that explain it.

Main Idea
Write a sentence that names the animal.

Detail
What is the animal covered with?

Detail
How big is the animal?

Detail
What color is the animal?

Detail
How does the animal move?

Detail
What does the animal do?

Name —————————————— **Date** ——————

Write an Informative Paragraph

You've picked an animal and organized your ideas. Now it's time to write your main idea/details paragraph.

Tips

Begin your paragraph with a sentence that introduces your animal.

Tell the most interesting facts about your animal.

Sum up your paragraph at the end.

Use compound subjects.

Name _____   **Date** _____

Compound Subjects

A Read each sentence. Then choose one of the words below it to fill in the blank and make a compound subject.

1. The frog and the _____ were friends.

   stone   alligator   island

2. Marilyn and _____ were frogs.

   chicken   Jessica   bird

3. Stones and _____ covered the ground.

   swim   enormous   pebbles

4. Grass and _____ grew on the island.

   weeds   dove   sea

5. The baby alligator and its _____ were happy.

   chicken   mother   weeds

B Write three sentences about animals. Use a compound subject in each sentence.

1. _____

   _____

2. _____

   _____

3. _____

   _____

Look in another book or a magazine for a sentence with a compound subject. Write the sentence in your Journal.

Name _____ **Date** _____

Words With Long *o*
Spelled *o-e* and *oe*

home	stone	hole	bone
dove	nose	toe	potatoes

Memory Tip

First with my n**ose**,
then with my t**oes**,
I d**ove** into the h**ole**.

A Fill in the missing vowels in the spelling words below.

1. h __ m __
2. h __ l __
3. n __ s __
4. b __ n __
5. d __ v __
6. potat __ __ s
7. t __ __
8. st __ n __

B Write the spelling word that answers the clue.
Circle the letters for the long vowel sound.

1. jumped headfirst into water _____

2. vegetables that grow in the ground _____

3. what you smell with _____

4. a small piece of rock _____

5. the place where you live _____

✔ Use for Grading

Name _____ **Date** _____

Similes

A Here are three similes from *An Extraordinary Egg*. Draw a line under the two things the author is comparing.

1. white like the snow

2. round like the full moon

3. as gentle as the whispering grass

> A simile compares two things. Similes use the word *like* or *as*. They make your writing colorful and interesting.

B Write the letter of the simile that best describes each thing.

1. ___ messy hair

2. ___ a loud voice

3. ___ a nice person

4. ___ the sky at sunset

a. like thunder

b. as red as a rose

c. as sweet as honey

d. like a bird's nest

C What would *you* say? Write your own similes.

1. My cold feet were like _____ .

2. The dinosaur was as tall as a _____ .

3. She can run fast like _____ .

4. The children were as noisy as _____ .

5. The clouds were like _____ .

 In your Journal, write your own similes for something *white*, something *round*, and a *gentle* voice.

✔ Use for Grading

Name _____ **Date** _____

Verbs in Action

Verbs are words that show action.

A Match the sentence subjects in the left column with the verb that fits from the right column. Draw a line to make the match.

1. The alligator   **a.** hopped
2. The happy mother   **b.** crawled
3. The swimmer   **c.** flew
4. The frog   **d.** dove
5. The bird   **e.** smiled

B Use the following verbs to complete each question below.

shout   climb

fly   jump   paddle

1. Were you able to _____ the mountain?
2. Can you _____ the boat across the lake?
3. Did you _____ out my name during the game?
4. Will you _____ on a plane to Mexico?
5. Can you _____ across the stream?

Name _____ **Date** _____

Reflect and Respond

A Read each question. Fill in the bubble in front of the correct answer.

1. What word best describes the frog named Jessica?

○ **a.** shy

○ **b.** curious

○ **c.** scared

2. What really hatched out of the extraordinary egg?

○ **a.** a chicken

○ **b.** a frog

○ **c.** an alligator

3. How did the mother alligator lose her egg and baby?

○ **a.** Jessica rolled the egg away.

○ **b.** A bird flew off with the egg.

○ **c.** The egg rolled down a hill.

B Read each question. Write your answer on the lines.

1. What big mistake did the frogs make in the story?

_____

_____

2. Why did Jessica and the baby alligator become good friends?

_____

_____

What Do You Think? How would you explain their mistake to the frogs? What advice would you give them?

✔ Use for Grading

Name _____ Date _____

Basketball Words

Story Words

basket in basketball, a net shaped like a basket open at the bottom

shoot to throw the ball at the basket

dribble to bounce the ball and move forward

hoop the round rim at the top of a basket

aim to point in the direction of a target

Everyday Language

dream a goal or aim

maybe perhaps

soccer a game played by kicking the ball into a goal

jump to push off with your legs into the air

proudly in a pleased, self-satisfied manner

 A Read each definition.
Fill in the blanks with the word.
Write one letter in each blank.

a. throw a ball at a basket

b. point in the direction of a target

c. bounce a ball and move forward

d. what a basketball player aims for

e. the rim at the top of the net

f. perhaps

g. a sport in which a ball is kicked into a goal

h. in a way that shows you're pleased with yourself

i. a goal

j. push off the ground into the air

$\_\,\_\,\_\,\_\,\_\,\_$
1

$\_\,\_\,\_$
2

$\_\,\_\,\_\,\_\,\_\,\_\,\_$
3

$\_\,\_\,\_\,\_\,\_$
4

$\_\,\_\,\_\,\_$
5

$\_\,\_\,\_\,\_$
6

$\_\,\_\,\_\,\_\,\_\,\_$
78

$\_\,\_\,\_\,\_\,\_\,\_\,\_$
9

$\_\,\_\,\_\,\_\,\_$
1011

$\_\,\_\,\_\,\_$

B Now write the numbered letters in the blanks below to solve this riddle!

Why did the basketball player bring a rope to the game?

She wanted to $\underset{1}{\_}\,\underset{2}{\_}\,\underset{3}{\_}\,\underset{4}{\_}\,\underset{5}{\_}\,\underset{6}{\_}\,\,\underset{7}{\_}\,\underset{8}{\_}\,\underset{9}{\_}\,\underset{10}{\_}\,\underset{11}{\_}$!

 Use for Grading

Name _____ **Date** _____

My Favorite Sport

A Read the paragraph below. Circle five words that look like Spanish words.

Michael's favorite sport is soccer. He practices every day after school. "Wow!" his friend exclaims, as Michael bounces the ball off his elbows, knees, heels, and toes in the center of the field. Michael hopes to be the captain of his soccer team one day.

B Read each sentence. On each line, write the word from the paragraph that matches the meaning in ( ).

1. I have a _____ place in the city. (the one I like best)

2. "What a beautiful present!" _____ Maria as she opens the box. (says something suddenly or with force, especially because you are excited)

3. My dog _____ catching a ball there. (does over and over to become skillful)

4. What I like best is a statue that's right in the _____ of the park. (middle)

5. It's a statue of a brave fire _____ and his dog. (leader)
   Maybe they'll build a statue of me and my dog someday!

Partners Find five other words in the story that are like Spanish words.

Name _____ **Date** _____

Long e – ie, y

A 1. Say the words and listen for long *e*. Draw a line under the words that have the sound of long *e*.

> The letters *ie* and *y* stand for the sound of long *e* in *chief* and *buddy*.

Allie	sunny	yes	chief
many	send	field	funny

2. Circle the letters that stand for long *e* in the words above.

B Finish the words in each sentence. Write *y* or *ie* in each blank.

1. I hurr_ to see if it's rain_ or snow_ , sunn_ or cloud_ .

2. As All_ _ hurr_ _ d to the ball f_ _ ld, she bel_ _ ved she saw the fire ch_ _ f.

3. The funn_ stor_ was about a girl who found a prett_ shin_ penn_.

Write the words you made in the correct column.

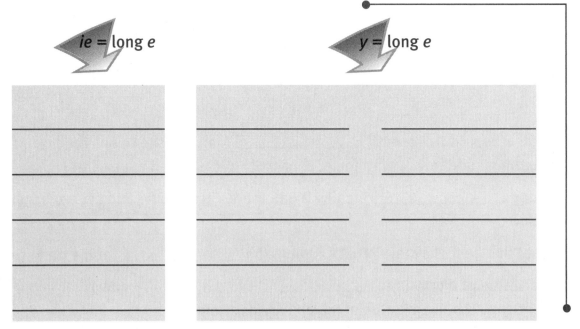

ie = long e

y = long e

 Make a list of six weather words that end in *y* with the sound of long *e*.

✔ Use for Grading

Name ——————————————— **Date** ———————

Remember

In a narrative paragraph, a person writes about an experience in the order it took place.

Use the chart to organize ideas.

A NARRATIVE PARAGRAPH

The Goal	What the Person Did to Reach His or Her Goal	Pronouns I Will Use

Name _____ **Date** _____

A Narrative Paragraph

You've planned your narrative. Now you can begin to write. Use your planning chart as you write.

Tips

Tell what your character wanted to do.
This will be your opening sentence.

Since you're writing about the past, use past-tense verbs.

Give details about what your character did to reach his or her goal.

Tell what finally happened to your character.

_____

_____

_____

_____

_____

_____

_____

_____

_____

_____

_____

Name _____ **Date** _____

Past-Tense Verbs

A Read each sentence. Circle the verb that belongs in the sentence.

1. Last Friday, it _____ .

   snowed   snow   snowing

2. We were so happy, we _____ up and down.

   jump   jumping   jumped

3. We dressed in our warm coats and boots and _____ our sleds up the hill.

   pull   pulled   pulling

4. We shouted and _____ as we rode down.

   laughing   laugh   laughed

5. We _____ it would snow again and again!

   hoped   hope   hoping

▲▲▲▲▲▲▲▲▲▲▲▲▲▲▲▲▲▲▲▲▲▲▲

B Write the past tense of each verb in ( ) by adding *-ed*. Remember this: if the verb ends in *e*, drop the *e* before you add *-ed*.

Yesterday I ...

(pick)   _____ apples,

(wash)   _____ them,

(slice)   _____ them,

(mix)   _____ flour and water to make dough,

(roll)   _____ out the dough,

(add)   _____ the apples, and

(bake)   _____ an apple pie.

Today I am eating it!

 Write two sentences about something you did for fun last week. Use verbs with *-ed*.

Name _____ **Date** _____

Long *e* Spelled *ie* and *y*

really	field	believe	hurry
chief	city	busy	piece

Memory Tip

You have to hurry in a busy city.

The letters *ie* and *y* can stand for the long *e* sound.

A Help Allie and Buddy make their baskets. Allie can score with words that have long *e* spelled *ie*. Buddy can score with words that have long *e* spelled *y*. Write the spelling words under the correct baskets.

_____   _____

_____   _____

_____   _____

_____   _____

B Write the spelling word that answers each clue.

1. It sounds the same as *peace*.   _____

2. It's not the country.   _____

3. Come on, _____ up!   _____

4. She's as _____ as a bee.   _____

5. It sounds like *beef*.   _____

6. It starts and ends like *find*.   _____

7. It means "to feel sure something is true." _____

8. It has the word *real* in it.   _____

✔ Use for Grading

Name _____ **Date** _____

Schwa

The *schwa* sound is the vowel you hear in an unaccented syllable. The *schwa* sound can be spelled in different ways. Say these words and listen for the syllable with the *schwa* sound. The syllable is circled.

| across | dribble | other | cousin | lemon |

A Draw a line from a syllable in column A to a syllable in column B to make a word with the *schwa* sound. Write each word you make on a line. The first one is done for you.

A	B
bub	er
wag	ble
lit	bout
moth	tle
a	in
rob	on

1. _____**bubble**_____
2. _____
3. _____
4. _____
5. _____
6. _____

B Say each word. Listen for the *schwa* sound. Fill in the blank with the word that has the *schwa* sound.

1. lemon   grape   I love _____ ices.

2. dime   nickel   I found a _____ on the sidewalk.

3. pear   apple   The _____ is very sweet.

4. summer   spring   My favorite season is _____.

5. yard   garden   I like to work in the _____.

 Find other words in the story that have the *schwa* sound.

✔ Use for Grading

Name _____ **Date** _____

Let's Get Together!

Some words are made by joining two smaller words together. These words are called *compound words*.

A Draw a line from a word in column 1 to a word in column 2 to make a compound word.

1	2
basket	ground
play	house
side	ball
fire	side
along	walk

B Write each compound word you made next to its meaning.

1. the part of the street you walk on _____

2. a sport _____

3. next to _____

4. an outdoor place with an area for sports _____

5. a building where engines are kept and firefighters wait until needed _____

C Make compound words. Write a word from the box that can be joined to each word below.

ball	slam	board	some

1. back _____

2. _____ thing

3. _____ dunk

4. volley _____

 Look in *Allie's Basketball Dream* for five compound words that are written as two separate words or with a hyphen. Write them in your Journal.

Name _____   **Date** _____

Reflect and Respond

Read each question. Fill in the bubble in front of the correct answer.

1. Why did the boys laugh at Allie?

- ○ **a.** She kept missing the basket.
- ○ **b.** The ball was too big for Allie.
- ○ **c.** Allie was making funny faces.

2. Allie's dream was

- ○ **a.** to play on her cousin Gwen's team.
- ○ **b.** to see all the professional games.
- ○ **c.** to be the best basketball player ever.

3. How did Allie learn to shoot baskets?

- ○ **a.** She watched the boys in the playground.
- ○ **b.** She kept trying until she could do it.
- ○ **c.** Her father showed her what to do.

4. Why did the boys applaud?

- ○ **a.** Allie had worked hard, and she made a perfect shot.
- ○ **b.** They knew Allie would be a baskeball star someday.
- ○ **c.** Allie won the game.

5. Which best describes the kind of person Allie is?

- ○ **a.** Allie is a very good ballplayer.
- ○ **b.** Allie works hard and doesn't give up.
- ○ **c.** Allie likes to show off.

What Do You Think? Will Allie's dream of becoming a basketball player come true? Explain your answer.

✔ Use for Grading

Name _____ Date _____

All About Dogs

Story Words

fetch to go get something

wag (wagging) to move something quickly from side to side

doghouse a small home for a dog

poodle a dog with thick, curly hair

leash (leashes) a strap to hold an animal

Everyday Words

backyard an open area behind a house

bicycle a vehicle with two wheels that you ride

treat (treats) a thing that you especially enjoy

chew to grind food between your teeth
chase to run after somebody or something

Can you solve this puzzle? From the boxes, write a word that goes with each puzzle clue.

Across

2. to run after something
4. a place to play outdoor games
6. You do this with food in your mouth.
7. a dog with curly hair
9. You eat these at snack time.

Down

1. Dogs do this after you throw a stick.
3. Dogs do this with their tails.
4. something you ride
5. A dog lives here.
8. You use this to walk a dog.

 In the book, find three other words that are about dogs. Write them in your Journal.

✔ Use for Grading

Name _____ Date _____

Make Connections

sofas   pedaling   minute   camera   limousine

A Think of a Spanish word that describes each picture below. Then, from the words above, choose a similar English word, and write it on the line.

1.

_____

2.

_____

3.

_____

4.

_____

5.

_____

B Interview a movie star. Use a word from above to complete each question.

1. Ms. Ramon, could I speak with you for one _____?

2. Do you enjoy _____ on a bicycle for exercise?

3. Is it true that you have many _____ in your living room?

4. Does your _____ have eight doors and hold twelve people?

5. Finally, can I take a picture of you with my _____?

Partners Find more words in the story that are similar to Spanish words.

Name _____ **Date** _____

Words With oo

The letters *oo* stand for the vowel sounds you hear in *moon* and *book*.

A Circle the word that names the picture. Then write the word on the line.

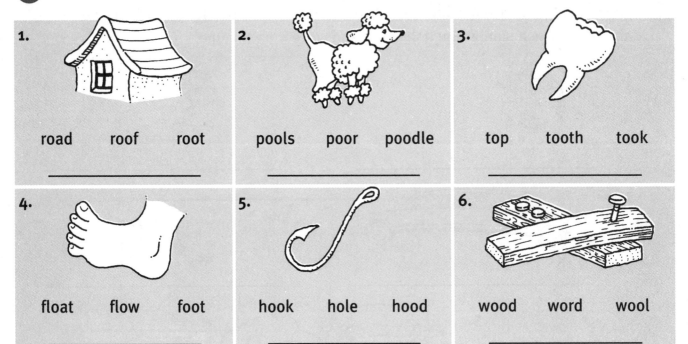

1. road   roof   root
_____

2. pools   poor   poodle
_____

3. top   tooth   took
_____

4. float   flow   foot
_____

5. hook   hole   hood
_____

6. wood   word   wool
_____

B Use the words you chose above to finish the sentences below. Then circle the letters that stand for the vowel sounds in *moon* and *book*.

1. I remember when my first _____ fell out.

2. My favorite dog is a _____ .

3. Ray was not wearing a shoe because he hurt his _____ .

4. Our doghouse is made out of _____ .

5. There was a leak in the _____ of the house.

6. You need a rod and a _____ to catch a fish.

 As you read the book, find three words spelled *oo*. Do they sound like the vowel sound in *moon* or like the vowel sound in *book*? Write them in your Journal.

✔ Use for Grading

Copyright © Scholastic Inc.

Name _____ **Date** _____

**emember**

Choose an animal. Use the chart to help you organize your fantasy paragraph.

A fantasy character is not real, but it can think, act, talk, and feel the way humans do.

Name of animal:

How does the fantasy animal look like a human?	**Where** does the animal live?	**What** does the animal do and say like a human?

Name _____ **Date** _____

Write a Fantasy Paragraph

You've picked an animal and organized your ideas. Now it's time to write your fantasy paragraph.

Tips

Use details to describe the animal.

 Tell where the animal lives.

How does the animal act like a human?

Use complete subjects and predicates.

Name _____ **Date** _____

Complete Subject and Predicate

Ⓐ Underline the complete subject and circle the complete predicate in each sentence.

Sample: <u>We</u> (went to the dog show.)

1. Dogs make great pets.

2. The black and white dog is mine.

3. I love taking my dog for a walk.

4. Sometimes dogs and cats are friends.

5. My friends and I tell stories about our dogs.

> **Tip**
>
> The complete subject includes all the words that tell who or what the sentence is about. The complete predicate includes all the words that tell what the subject does or is.

Ⓑ Write three sentences. Underline the complete subject and circle the complete predicate in each sentence.

1. _____

_____

2. _____

_____

3. _____

_____

With a partner, go back to the story, and find two sentences. Take turns pointing out the complete subjects and predicates. Write the sentences in your Journal.

✔ Use for Grading

Name _____ Date _____

Words With *oo* as in *school* and *book*

look	cool	tool	shook
took	cook	pool	poodle

Memory Tip

The p**oo**dle was so c**oo**l, everyone t**oo**k a l**oo**k.

A The letters *oo* can stand for the vowel sounds you hear in *school* and *book*. Sort the words in the box using these vowel sounds.

Words With the Same Vowel Sound as in *school*

_____

_____

_____

_____

Words With the Same Vowel Sound as in *book*

_____

_____

_____

_____

B Write the spelling word that answers the clue. Circle the letters for the vowel sound.

1. what you do to see something _____

2. a person who makes food _____

3. a place to swim _____

4. the past tense of *take* _____

5. what a farmer needs to work _____

6. the opposite of *warm* _____

7. an animal you'd see at a dog show _____

8. the past tense of *shake* _____

✔ Use for Grading

Name _____ **Date** _____

Consonant Clusters -tch and tw-

The letters **tch** stand for one sound. It is the sound you hear at the end of **catch**.
The letters **tw** stand for two sounds. You hear them at the beginning of **twin**.

A Say the word that names each picture. Draw a line from the picture to the correct word.

twins

twelve

watch

match

twenty

In the words above, circle the letters that stand for the sound at the end of *catch*. Draw a line under the letters that stand for the sounds you hear at the beginning of *twin*.

B Solve the riddles. The answers to the odd numbers are words that begin with *tw*. The answers to the even numbers are words that end with *tch*.

1. It's noontime. _____

2. You use it to light candles. _____

3. It's what you get when you add ten and ten. _____

4. It tells you the time. _____

5. Two children in the same family who were born at the same time. _____

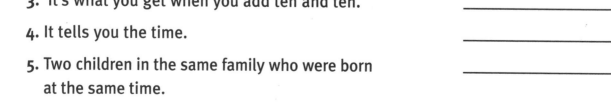 In your Journal, write riddles for two words that begin with **tw** and two that end with **tch**.

 ✔ Use for Grading

Name _____ **Date** _____

Word Pictures

Word pictures can make a story fun to read. They can also help you figure out the meaning of a word or phrase.

shake hands
next-door neighbor
chase our tails

 A Write the word or phrase from the box that goes with each picture.

1.

_____

2.

_____

3.

_____

B Now create your own word pictures. Write a word or phrase from the box above in the spaces below. Then use colored pencils, pens, or crayons to make word pictures.

1. _____

2. _____

Name _____   **Date** _____

Reflect and Respond

A Read each question. Fill in the bubble in front of the best answer.

1. How do you know this book is a fantasy?

○ **a.** The pictures are in color.

○ **b.** The boy owns a bicycle.

○ **c.** The dogs can talk.

2. Why does the boy follow his dog?

○ **a.** He can't believe his dog is wearing a tuxedo.

○ **b.** He's afraid his dog is sick.

○ **c.** He thinks his dog might be digging in a neighbor's yard.

3. What does the boy find out about his dog?

○ **a.** He serves water and biscuits at The Doghouse.

○ **b.** He's the boss at The Doghouse.

○ **c.** He has no friends at The Doghouse.

B Read each question. Write your answer on the lines.

1. Why do dogs enjoy The Doghouse?

_____

_____

2. How does the boy feel when he gets his picture taken?

_____

_____

What Do You Think? What might the boy and his dog talk about the next day?

✔ Use for Grading

Name _____ **Date** _____

Let's Go Harvesting

Story Words

crop a plant grown for food

labor to work hard

meadow a field of grass

harvest the crops that are collected

peach soft, round, sweet fruit with fuzzy skin

Everyday Words

worker a person who does a job

matter to be of importance

belong to be part of

remember to recall or to bring back to mind

camp an outdoor area with tents or cabins where people stay

A Check the correct meaning for each word.

1. **peach**	_ hard, sour fruit	_ soft, sweet fruit	_ small, blue fruit
2. **labor**	_ to have fun	_ to rest	_ to work
3. **meadow**	_ field	_ road	_ mountain
4. **crop**	_ plant	_ pet	_ place to stay
5. **harvest**	_ apple trees	_ peaches in baskets	_ glass of milk

B Make up sentences that use two vocabulary words.

camp	remember	1. _____
belong	workers	2. _____
harvest	matter	3. _____

Find three other words in the book that tell about harvesting.
Write the words in your Journal.

✔ Use for Grading

Name _____   **Date** _____

The Hidden Treasure

A Read the paragraph below, and find five
words that look like Spanish words. Circle the words.

> At the fruit stand, Tracy picks up a piece of
> paper. It is a map to find a hidden treasure! There is
> a tiny photograph of a house where the treasure is.
> Now Tracy has a problem. Should she try to find the
> treasure? Should she forget about it? At important
> times like this, Tracy likes to talk to her dog, Felix.
> This helps Tracy think more clearly.

B Write the circled words next to the correct definitions below.

1. used to get from one place to another place   _____
2. apples, peaches, and bananas   _____
3. a difficulty that needs to be solved   _____
4. a picture   _____
5. worth taking seriously   _____

Partners Find words in *Amelia's Road* that are similar to Spanish words.

Name _____ **Date** _____

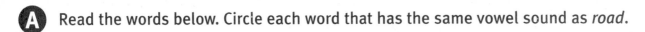

Long o (o, oa, ow)

> The letters *o*, *oa*, and *ow* stand
> for the long *o* sound you hear in *road*.

A Read the words below. Circle each word that has the same vowel sound as *road*.

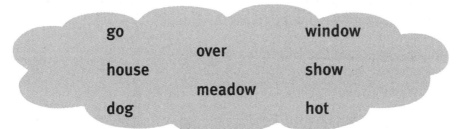

go   window

over

house   show

meadow

dog   hot

B Read each sentence. Fill in the blank with one of the words you circled above. Then circle the letters in each word that stand for the long *o* sound.

1. The sheep are in the _____ .

2. Open the _____ and let in the warm air.

3. Can you _____ me how to do it?

4. The airplane flew _____ the hill.

5. Where will you _____ after school?

 As you read the book, find at least three words with long *o* spelled *o*, *oa*, or *ow*. Write them in your Journal.

✔ Use for Grading

Name _____ **Date** _____

Descriptions help people picture places in their minds. Plan to write a description of your favorite place. Use this chart to organize your ideas.

My Favorite Place

_____

Where is the place?	What does it look like?	Why is it fun to spend time there?

Name _____ **Date** _____

Write a Description of a Place

You've picked a favorite place and organized your ideas. Now, write your description.

Tips

Name your
favorite place.

Use specific details
to describe it.

Make sure you place
adjectives before nouns.

Tell why you like to
spend time there.

_____

_____

_____

_____

_____

_____

_____

_____

_____

_____

_____

_____

Name _____ **Date** _____

Adjectives

A Read each sentence and the words below it.
Circle the adjective that completes the sentence.

1. Hector was a _____ basketball player.

   tall   tailor   tore

2. The child needed _____ help crossing the street.

   eggs   extra   ended

3. I think Mia is a _____ runner.

   finely   fell   fast

> **Tip**
>
> Adjectives are words that describe a person, place, or thing. Writers use adjectives to create vivid word pictures.

B Read the following sentences. Underline the adjectives.

Sample: She painted a <u>pretty white</u> house with a <u>great big</u> tree in the <u>front</u> yard.

1. I saw a pretty brown fox in the field.

2. The workers ate big, juicy peaches.

3. It was a hot, dry, and sunny day.

4. As Serena opened the rusty old door, it made a loud squeak.

5. We tossed pebbles as we walked along the long, straight, and quiet road.

 Write two sentences describing your favorite food. Use three adjectives.

Name _____ **Date** _____

Words With Long *o* Spelled *o, oa, ow*

go   nobody   window   road

over   meadow   show   boat

Memory Tip

From my wind**ow**,
I can see **o**ver
the r**oa**d.

A Write the spelling word that names each picture. Then circle the letters that stand for the long *o* sound.

1.

_____

2.

_____

3.

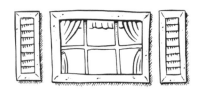

_____

4.

_____

B Sort the spelling words by the letters that stand for the long *o* sound. Write the words in the chart below.

Words With Long *o* Spelled *o*	Words With Long *o* Spelled *oa*	Words With Long *o* Spelled *ow*
_____	_____	_____
_____	_____	_____

✔ Use for Grading

Name _____ **Date** _____

Initial *h* and *r*

The letter *h* stands for the sound you hear at the beginning of *home*. The letter *r* stands for the sound you hear at the beginning of *run*.

A Say the word that names each picture. If the word begins with the *h* sound, draw a line from the picture to the letter *h*. If the word begins with the *r* sound, draw a line to the letter *r*.

hard	road	hear	right	ride
run	rose	hurry	hat	home

B Say each word. Then write the word from the box that rhymes with it.

1. bat _____
2. nose _____
3. comb _____
4. card _____
5. snowed _____

6. fun _____
7. tried _____
8. worry _____
9. year _____
10. kite _____

 Find five words in the story with two syllables that begin with *h* or *r*, such as *hurry* and *rabbit*. Write them in your Journal.

✔ Use for Grading

Name _____   **Date** _____

Around and Around

Around and around is a phrase that means "to go in a circle many times." Every day you see things that move around and around.

A   Look at the pictures below. Draw lines from the center circle to the pictures of things that move around and around.

Around and Around

B   Write a sentence for each of the pictures above that shows something going around and around. Be sure to include the phrase *around and around* in each sentence.

1. _____

   _____

2. _____

   _____

3. _____

   _____

Name _____ **Date** _____

Reflect and Respond

A Read each question. Fill in the bubble next to the best answer.

1. Why does Amelia hate roads?
   ○ **a.** They are too bumpy.
   ○ **b.** They lead to labor camps.
   ○ **c.** They make the car dusty.

2. What does Amelia want more than anything else?
   ○ **a.** She wants a place to settle down and call home.
   ○ **b.** She wants a best friend and a dog.
   ○ **c.** She wants a new pair of shoes and pants.

3. What does Amelia do in Mrs. Ramos's classroom?
   ○ **a.** She raises her hand and answers a question.
   ○ **b.** She forgets her books and goes home.
   ○ **c.** She draws a pretty picture and gets a red star.

B Read each question. Write your answer on the lines.

1. What does Amelia find at the end of the accidental road?

   _____

   _____

2. What does Amelia do with the old metal box?

   _____

   _____

What Do You Think? How will Amelia feel when she returns to the tree next year?
Explain your answer.

✔ Use for Grading

Name _____ **Date** _____

Cinderella

Story Words

stepsister a daughter of your stepfather or stepmother by a former marriage

spell an enchanted state caused by magic

ball a fancy party where there is dancing

wand a thin stick with magical powers

flipper a wide, flat rubber shoe used by people for swimming or diving

Everyday Words

rags old, worn-out clothing

midnight 12 o'clock at night

cozy comfortable or snug

chores jobs you have to do around the house

tears drops that fall from your eyes when you cry

A Fill in each blank with a word from the boxes.

1. Who did the princess dance with at the _____ ?

2. The magician waved his magic _____ , and the rabbit reappeared.

3. Maria wanted a new dress so that she wouldn't have to wear her old _____ to the ball.

4. What _____ do you do around the house?

5. Helen was so sad that _____ fell down her cheeks.

B Check the correct meaning for each word.

1. **midnight:** _ playtime   _ nighttime   _ lunchtime

2. **cozy:** _ happy   _ uncomfortable   _ relaxed

3. **stepsister:** _ relative   _ teacher   _ cousin

4. **spell:** _ a sad condition   _ a happy condition   _ a magical condition

5. **flipper:** _ a kind of dancer   _ a kind of hat   _ a kind of shoe

 In the book, find three words that tell about Cinderella. Write them in your Journal.

✔ Use for Grading

Name _____ **Date** _____

The Birthday Party

A Read the paragraph below, and find five words that look like Spanish words. Circle the words.

When Annie picked up the mail, she found an invitation to her friend's birthday party. "Mother," she called, "I need a new dress for this party!" Her mother showed her some delicate white lace and offered to sew it around the collar and sleeves of Annie's old party dress. "It will look so natural and pretty, don't you think?" Annie nodded. She was so excited all week that she couldn't pay attention in class. Finally, it was Saturday.

B Write the words you circled next to their correct definition.

1. dainty or full of small details   _____

2. after a long time   _____

3. concentration and careful thought   _____

4. a card asking you to come to a party   _____

5. something that is without false qualities   _____

Partners Find more words in *Cinderella Penguin* that are similar to Spanish words.

Name _____ **Date** _____

s-Clusters str-, sn-, sw-

Some words begin with two or three consonants that blend together.
Most of the time, each letter keeps its own sound.

snail

swim

swing

snake

string

A Write a word from the box that names each picture. Then
circle the s-clusters str-, sn-, sw- in each word.

1. _____

2. _____

3. _____

4. _____

5. _____

B Read each riddle below. Choose the correct answer, and write it on the line.

1. It has the same two-letter cluster as *snap*. You eat this when you are a little hungry.

What is it? _____   snack   snail   snore

2. It has the same three-letter cluster as *strap*. A car follows this to go places.

What is it? _____   stroll   street   straight

3. It has the same two-letter cluster as *swell*. You and a friend can do this

with baseball cards.

What is it? _____   sweat   sweep   swap

4. It has the same three-letter cluster as *straw*. Fish can live here.

What is it? _____   streak   stump   stream

5. It has the same two-letter cluster as *sweet*. You can ride on one in the park.

What is it? _____   swing   swamp   saddle

 Look for three more words in the story that begin with the s-clusters str-, sn-, sw-.

✔ Use for Grading

Name _____ **Date** _____

GET READY TO WRITE!

You have chosen your subjects. Now use the chart below to help you organize your ideas.

Remember

A compare/contrast paragraph includes both the similarities and the differences between the two characters you choose.

How Does the Person Look?

What Kinds of Things Does the Person Do?

How Does the Person Act Around Other People?

Name of Character One:

_____

Name of Character Two:

_____

Name ——————————————— **Date** ———————————

Write a Compare/Contrast Paragraph

You've picked two people and organized your ideas. Now it's time to write your compare/contrast paragraph.

Tips

• Identify the two characters you are writing about.

Tell how they are alike. Tell how they are different.

Use details and examples to illustrate your points.

Use subject pronouns.

•

_____

_____

_____

_____

_____

_____

_____

_____

_____

_____

_____

Name _____   **Date** _____

Subject Pronouns

A Circle the subject pronoun in each of these sentences.

Sample: (We) live on the same block.

1. She is my oldest friend.

2. No, thanks, I don't want any more potatoes.

3. He laughed out loud during the movie.

4. Are you coming to my house today?

5. They played baseball until dark.

Tip

Pronouns are words that replace nouns. Subject pronouns replace the subject of a sentence. They are *I, you, he, she, it, we, they.*

ha ha!

B Underline the complete subject in each of the sentences below. Then rewrite the sentence by substituting a subject pronoun for the word you underlined.

1. The boy liked to make up puzzles.

_____

_____

2. Maria rode her horse across the field.

_____

_____

3. My brother and sister are twins.

_____

_____

 Go back to the story, and find sentences using three different subject pronouns. Read the sentences aloud, and write them in your Journal.

Name _____ **Date** _____

Words With *s*-Clusters *str-*, *sn-*, *sw-*

A Draw lines from one puzzle piece to the other to make the spelling words. Write the words you make on the lines.

stroke   street   stretch   snack
snatch   snip   swing   swim

1. str — im _____

2. sw — ip _____

3. str — ack _____

4. sn — etch _____

5. sw — oke _____

6. str — ing _____

7. sn — atch _____

8. sn — eet _____

B Write the spelling word that answers each clue.

1. You get all wet when you do this. _____

2. You do this after you've been sitting a long time. _____

3. A barber does this to cut hair. _____

4. A batter does this with a baseball bat. _____

5. This word rhymes with *patch*. _____

6. This has houses, stores, or other buildings along it. _____

7. You eat this when you get hungry. _____

8. This word rhymes with *poke*. _____

✔ Use for Grading

Name _____ **Date** _____

Initial Consonant v

The letter *v* makes the sound you hear at the beginning of the word *very*.

A Say the name of each pair of pictures. Circle the one that has the initial *v* sound as in *voice*.

1.

2.

3.

4.

B From the box, write the initial *v* word that goes with each pair.

1. drum, horn, _____

2. pants, jacket, _____

3. camera, film, _____

4. fruit, vegetables, _____

5. look, see, _____

6. plant, bush, _____

video	vitamins
vine	vest
view	violin

 Think of three other things you could find at home or school that begin with the letter *v*. Write them in your Journal.

✔ Use for Grading

Name _____ **Date** _____

Same Word, Different Meaning

A From the box, write the word that goes with each of these pictures. There are six pictures, but only three words, so you'll have to use each word twice.

kind	ball	glass

1.

_____

2.

_____

3.

_____

4.

_____

5.

Types of Animals
Mammals
Reptiles
Birds

_____

6.

_____

B Write three sentences, each using one of the three words in the box. After each sentence, write the number of the picture above that is closest to the meaning of your sentence.

Sample: *I broke my favorite glass.* (#6)

1. _____

2. _____

3. _____

Name _____ **Date** _____

Reflect and Respond

A Read each question. Fill in the bubble in front of the best answer.

1. What does the Great Fairy Penguin do?

○ **a.** She turns a pumpkin into a coach.

○ **b.** She changes Cinderella's name.

○ **c.** She teaches the Prince a magic word.

2. Why does Cinderella leave the ball before midnight?

○ **a.** She has another date.

○ **b.** She is very tired.

○ **c.** Her party clothes will turn back into rags.

3. How do you know this is a fairy tale?

○ **a.** It has penguins in it.

○ **b.** Someone casts a magic spell.

○ **c.** There is a big dance in a palace.

B Read the questions. Write your answers on the lines.

1. How does Cinderella Penguin feel when her stepmother and stepsisters leave for the ball?

_____

2. How do her stepmother and stepsisters feel when the glass flipper fits perfectly on Cinderella Penguin's foot?

_____

What Do You Think? Do you think Cinderella Penguin will ever invite her stepmother and stepsisters to visit at the palace? Explain your answer.

✔ Use for Grading

Name _____ **Date** _____

Stargazing

Story Words

stargazer a person who watches the night sky

atmosphere the layers of air around Earth

galaxy a group of billions of stars

constellation a group of stars that forms the outline of a person, animal, or object

discovery something that has been found

Everyday Words

sky the arch of air over Earth

clear free of clouds

shine to give off bright light

twinkle to shine with quick flashes of light

bright giving off a strong or intense light

Can you solve this puzzle? Write a word from the box that goes with each puzzle clue.

Across

2. something that has been found

5. shining with lots of light

7. to shine with quick flashes of light

8. without clouds

10. the layers of air around Earth

Down

1. a group of stars that form a certain shape

3. the arch of air you see when you look up

4. a person who looks for stars at night

6. a group of billions of stars

9. to give off light

 From the book, find three other words about looking at stars. Write them in your Journal.

✔ Use for Grading

Name _____ **Date** _____

Language Bridge

planet	million	famous	astronomer	color

A On the line, write an English word from the box.

Remember
Thinking of the words in Spanish will help you to remember the words in English.

1. _____

2. _____

3. _____

4. _____

5.

_____

B Use words from the box to fill in the blanks in these sentences.

1. I would like to be a _____ baseball player someday.

2. Green has always been my favorite _____ .

3. Jupiter is the largest _____ in our solar system.

4. My older brother is an _____ .

5. A _____ dollars is a lot of money.

Partners Look for additional English words that look like Spanish words.

✔ Use for Grading

Name _____ **Date** _____

Long *i*

The letters *igh* and *y* stand for the long *i* sound you hear in the English word *I*.

A Read the words below. Circle each word that has the same vowel sound as the English word *I*.

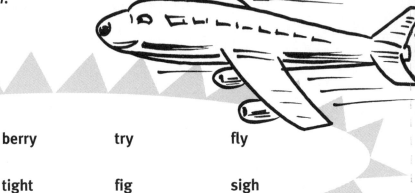

bright   berry   try   fly

typical   tight   fig   sigh

B Fill in the blanks with one of the words you circled above. Then circle the letters in each word that make the long *i* sound.

1. Ouch! My shoes are too _____!

2. Did you ever _____ in an airplane?

3. When the sun is _____, I wear sunglasses.

4. We _____ when we are very tired.

5. I like to _____ new games on the computer.

As you read the book, find other words with the long *i* sound spelled *igh* and *y*. Write them in your Journal.

✔ Use for Grading

Name _____   **Date** _____

In your newspaper article, you need to answer the questions *Who? What? Where? When? Why?* and *How?* Use the chart to help you organize your information.

Who? _____

_____

What? _____

_____

Where? _____

_____

When? _____

_____

Why? _____

_____

How? _____

_____

Name _____ **Date** _____

Write a Newspaper Article

You've gathered factual information and organized your ideas. Now it's time to write your newspaper article.

Tips

State your main idea or topic (who/what).

Include where and when it happened.

State why it happened.

Make sure the article includes at least one compound sentence.

Name _____   **Date** _____

Words With Long *i* Spelled *igh* or *y*

night	sight	sky
bright	try	fly
light		cry

Memory Tip

Don't **cry** at **night**; **try** to turn on a **light**.

A Sort the spelling words by the letters they use to make the long *i* sound.

Words With *igh*	Words With *y*

B Write the spelling word that answers the clue. Circle the letters that make the long *i* sound.

1. what a bird uses wings for _____

2. what you turn on when the room is dark _____

3. what you do when you're very sad _____

4. when you usually sleep _____

5. what you sometimes have to do over and over again _____

6. what the sunlight is _____

7. where the rain falls from _____

8. what your eyes give you _____

✔ Use for Grading

Name _____ **Date** _____

Compound Sentences

A Circle each simple sentence, and underline each connecting word.

Sample: We (saddled the horses,) and (we went for a long ride.)

1. Eduardo wrote a story, and his teacher read it to the class.

2. My brother will be on time, or my sister will call.

3. I want to play, but I have to go to the dentist.

4. Rocio went to Italy, and then she went to Egypt.

5. His father gave him an apple, but his grandfather gave him a banana.

B Write three compound sentences. Circle the independent clauses, and underline the connecting word in each sentence.

1. _____

_____

_____

2. _____

_____

_____

3. _____

_____

_____

 Look through other books you have read, and find three compound sentences. Read the sentences aloud, and write them in your Journal along with the titles of the books.

✔ Use for Grading

Copyright © Scholastic Inc.

Name _____ **Date** _____

Phonics: ar, or

A Say the word that names each picture. Draw a circle around the ones that have the *ar* sound as in *far*. Make a line under the ones that have the *or* sound as in *for*.

B Use a word from the box to finish each sentence.
The word you write will rhyme with the word in dark type.

art	far
yard	corn
short	born

1. A **star** is very, very _____ .

2. My kitten was _____ on an April **morn**.

3. It's not **hard** to clean our _____ .

4. Is the ride to the **airport** long or _____ ?

5. Blow your **horn** when it's time to eat the _____ !

6. That apple **tart** is a work of _____ .

 Find other words in *Stargazers* with *ar* and *or*.

✔ Use for Grading

Name _____ **Date** _____

Is It -y or -ish?

A Read each sentence and the words below it.
Circle the noun that you can make an adjective
by adding *y*. Then add the *y*, and write the word
in the blank.

Remember
You can add a -y to a
noun to make it into an
adjective. You can add
-ish to make it mean "a
little bit of" or "like
something."

1. It was a dark and _____ night.

   wild   wet   storm

2. That was a _____ thing to do.

   sneak   mean   bad

3. We raced down a steep, _____ road.

   wet   rock   curved

B Read each sentence and the words below it. Circle the
word that you can change by adding *-ish*. Then add the *-ish*,
and write the word in the blank.

1. He dyed his hair a _____ color.

   different   yellow   strange

2. He cried so much we thought he was _____ .

   unhappy   silly   baby

C Write an original sentence for two words
of your choice. Use *-y* or *-ish*.

_____

_____

_____

 Bluish, milky, and *cloudy* come from the book. Write your own sentences using
each of these words.

Name _____ **Date** _____

Reflect and Respond

A Read each question. Fill in the bubble next to the best answer.

1. Why do stars look so small?

○ **a.** Because they are only the size of a peach

○ **b.** Because they are far away

○ **c.** Because there is too much sunlight to see them

2. What is a constellation?

○ **a.** It is a group of stars.

○ **b.** It is the brightest star in any group.

○ **c.** It is a group of stargazers.

3. Why do people go to a planetarium?

○ **a.** To find out about dinosaurs

○ **b.** To find out about stars

○ **c.** To find out about plants

B Read each question. Write your answer on the lines.

1. How did constellations get their names?

_____

_____

2. Name two tools that stargazers use to help them see the stars.

_____

What Do You Think? What is the best part of being an astronomer or stargazer? What is the worst part? Explain your answer.

✔ Use for Grading

Name _____ Date _____

Birthday Celebrations

Story Words

celebrate to mark a happy event with special activities

decoration(s) a pretty or colorful object or design used to brighten up something

surprise something you don't expect

candle(s) a thin piece of wax around a string that is burned to give light

swap the practice of exchanging one thing for another

Everyday Words

relative a person of the family

birthday the day of the year when a person was born

present a gift

cake a dessert made of sweet dough covered with icing

think to form ideas; to have an idea or opinion

A Check the correct meaning for each word.

1. cake: __ a drink __ a treat __ a person

2. relative: __ someone from your family __ a friend __ someone

3. decoration: __ makes something pretty __ makes something clean __ makes something bigger

4. candle: __ something you eat __ something you light __ something you wear

5. present: __ a gift __ a gate __ a girl

B Fill in each blank with a word from the boxes.

1. How old will you be on your next _____?

2. Our team will _____ if we win the game.

3. Don't tell Miriam about the party because it's a _____.

4. Do you want to _____ your baseball cards with me?

5. What do you _____ the correct answer is?

Find other words in the book that tell about birthday celebrations. Write them in your Journal.

✔ Use for Grading

Name ———————————————— **Date** ——————————

The Trip

family   animal   reunion   tourist   idea

A Read the paragraph below, and find five words that look like Spanish words. Circle the words.

Last week my family took a trip to Mexico. It was my sister's idea. She wanted to see her best friend, so our parents spoke on the phone and arranged for a reunion. I wanted to bring our dog with us, but my Dad said it was too hard to bring an animal across the border. I was so excited to see everything, I felt like a tourist!

B Use the words you circled to fill in the blanks.

1. In ten years, let's have a class _____.

2. Arturo would love an _____, but his mother said no.

3. I have a good _____ for my next writing assignment.

4. The _____ went on a cruise.

5. When I grow up, I'll visit my _____ often.

Partners Find additional new words in *The Birthday Swap* that are similar to Spanish words.

✔ Use for Grading

Name _____ Date _____

Consonant Clusters *ng* and *nk*

The letters *ng* stand for the sound you hear at the end of the word *swing*. The letters *nk* stand for the sound you hear at the end of the word *ink*.

A Circle the word that names the picture. Then write the word on the line.

1. wink
wing
whip

2. drink
drip
dunk

3. rang
rink
ring

_____

_____

_____

4. jungle
junk
joke

5. sing
string
sink

6. king
kink
cling

_____

_____

_____

B Use the words from above to fill in the blanks in these sentences. Then circle the letters that make the ending sounds in *swing* and *ink*.

1. Wash your hands in the _____.

2. Do you think the _____ of the bird is broken?

3. The people do not vote for a _____.

4. That may be _____ to you, but I can use some of those things.

5. When it's hot, Juan's favorite _____ is cold water.

6. My sister has a gold _____ that she never takes off.

 As you read the book, find two words ending with *-ng* and two words ending with *-nk*. Write them in your Journal.

✔ Use for Grading

Name _____ **Date** _____

GET READY TO WRITE!

In your paragraph you need to arrange events in the order they happened, building up to the main event. Use the chart to help you organize your paragraph.

Remember

A paragraph ordered by sequence uses signal words to keep track of events.

Event: _____

What led up to the main event?	What was the main event?	What happened after the main event?
1.	1.	1.
2.	2.	2.
3.	3.	3.

Name _____ **Date** _____

Write a Paragraph Ordered in Sequence

You've chosen a memorable event and organized your ideas. Now it's time to write a paragraph ordered by sequence.

Tips

Use a time word in your first sentence. Name the event.

Identify who is involved in the event.

Use sequence words to move from one sentence to the next.

Use adverbs.

State your conclusion.

_____

_____

_____

_____

_____

_____

_____

_____

_____

_____

_____

✔ Use for Grading

Name _____ **Date** _____

Adverbs

A Circle the adverb or adverbs in each sentence.

1. Ana ate quickly and ran off to play.

2. My parents were at work then.

3. Are you listening carefully?

4. The new car runs smoothly.

5. The man spoke angrily; later he was sorry.

Tip

Adverbs are words that modify verbs. They answer the questions *How? When?* or *Where?* Most adverbs that tell *how* end in *-ly*. Adverbs that tell *when* are often signal words: *first, later, before, while, then.*

B Write three sentences. Use at least one adverb in each sentence. Circle all the adverbs, and draw an arrow to show what verb they modify.

1. _____

_____

_____

2. _____

_____

_____

3. _____

_____

_____

With a partner, go back to the story, and find three adverbs. Read the sentences aloud to your partner. Then write them in your Journal.

✔ Use for Grading

Name _____ **Date** _____

Words With the Ending Sounds of *ring* and *sink*

thing sing think pink
string spring drink blink

Memory Tip

I think spring comes in a blink and ends in a string of flowers.

A Write the spelling word that answers each clue.

1. If your birthday is in April, it's in this season. _____

2. When you close and open your eyes, you do this. _____

3. You do this when you have to solve a problem. _____

4. Many roses are this color. _____

5. You can use this to tie up a package. _____

6. You want this when you are thirsty. _____

7. You can do this with a song. _____

8. A general name for any object. _____

B Sort the spelling words by the letters they end with.

Words With the Same Ending Sound as *ring*

Words With the Same Ending Sound as *sink*

✔ Use for Grading

Name _____ **Date** _____

The Long a Sound

Sometimes the letters *ei* combine to make the long *a* sound that you hear in the word *sleigh*.

A Fill in the blanks with the word that has a long *a* sound.

neighbor	friend
free	freight
weight	fat
three	eight

1. Yesterday my _____ baked me a cake.

2. The old man rode on a _____ train.

3. My brother eats a lot because he wants to gain _____.

4. Maria's dog had _____ puppies.

B The answers to the following questions all have the long *a* sound. Choose your answers from this list, and write them in the blanks.

eight	man
weight	head
seven	neighbor
freight	animals

1. What is half of sixteen? _____

2. Who lives next door to you? _____

3. What can a train carry besides people? _____

4. What does the doctor measure besides your height? _____

C Use one of the *ei* words to complete each rhyme.

1. There is no number I really hate,

   But my favorite number has always been _____.

2. A calendar tells me the date,

   But I need a scale to tell my _____.

3. On a boat you carry bait,

   But on a train you carry _____.

4. When you work hard, it takes much labor.

   If you need help, then ask your _____.

freight

neighbor

weight

eight

✔ Use for Grading

Name _____   **Date** _____

Signal Words

A Circle the signal word that belongs in the blank.

1. He woke up rested _____ a short nap.

   before   after   while

2. First eat your dinner; _____ you can have dessert.

   later   during   again

3. The teacher was late; she arrived _____ we did.

   before   next   after

4. Don't give up; try _____.

   next   last   again

5. _____ I am ten, but that summer I was only five.

   Then   Now   When

B Here are three signal words: *first, while, later.* Write your own sentences using each of these words.

1. _____

   _____

2. _____

   _____

3. _____

   _____

Pick two signal words you used on this page. In your Journal, write two related sentences using them, showing in what order two things happened.

Name _____ **Date** _____

Reflect and Respond

A Read each question. Fill in the bubble next to the best answer.

1. Who knew about Lori's surprise party in advance?

○ **a.** only Lori

○ **b.** only Lori's sister

○ **c.** everyone but Lori

2. Why did Mom make Lori a new dress?

○ **a.** The whole family was going to church.

○ **b.** Mom wanted Lori to wear something special to her party.

○ **c.** Mom was bored.

3. Why did Lori fall asleep?

○ **a.** She was tired of playing with her puppy.

○ **b.** It was very late at night.

○ **c.** Nobody would dance with her.

B Read each question. Then write your answer on the lines.

1. How would you describe Lori's family?

_____

_____

2. How does Lori feel when she opens the box and sees the puppy?

_____

_____

What Do You Think? What do you think Lori and her family might talk about the day after the birthday party? Explain your answer.

✔ Use for Grading

Name _____ **Date** _____

Dog Guides

Story Words

trained to teach new skills

blind having no sense of sight

guide(s) someone or something that leads

handle part that is held or turned with the hand

command(s) an order or instruction

Everyday Words

important of great meaning or value

smart clever and quick in thinking

obey do as commanded or instructed

forward toward the front; ahead

strong powerful; in good health

A Complete each sentence with a word from the boxes.

1. Dogs can be trained to help people who are _____ .

2. The weather report is very _____ if you are planning a picnic.

3. If you are a coach, you probably have _____ a runner for a marathon.

4. If your dog can open the door and bring in the paper, your dog is very _____ .

5. We typed several _____ into the computer, but it still didn't work.

B Make up a sentence with the two vocabulary words in each row.

1. smart   strong   _____

_____

2. guide   handle   _____

_____

3. obey   forward   _____

_____

 Find three other words in the book that tell about dog guides.
Write the words in your Journal.

✔ Use for Grading

Name _____   **Date** _____

Rescue Dogs

A Read the paragraph below, and find five words that look like Spanish words. Circle the words.

During our visit, the police taught us about the work of rescue dogs. The dogs must learn many lessons. The dogs are trained to follow directions. The police depend on rescue dogs to help them do their work.

B Write each word that you circled in a sentence below.

1. German shepherds make excellent _____ dogs.

2. Dad is helping me with my English _____ .

3. What are the _____ to get to the school?

4. My cousin Rachel is going to _____ me for a few days.

5. The teacher can _____ on her students for help.

Partners Find more words in the story that are similar to Spanish words.

✔ Use for Grading

Name _____ **Date** _____

Consonant Clusters -nd and -nt

The letters *nd* and *nt* stand for the ending sounds you hear in *hand* and *went*.

A Write the letters *nd* or *nt* on the lines to complete the story.

Yesterday I spe_ _ all day with my frie_ _. We had a
wonderful time. In the morning, we walked arou_ _ town and we_ _
to play at the playgrou_ _. For lunch we ate a large amou_ _ of
fruit and cheese! In the afternoon we played in the sa_ _ at the
beach. I was so tired at the e_ _ of the day that I fell asleep as soon
as I got home. I learned an importa_ _ lesson yesterday.
Never do so much in one day!

B Figure out the equations below to make new words. Write the words on the lines.
Circle either the *nd* or *nt* ending in each new word.

1. send - *nd* + *nt* = _____

2. want - *nt* + *nd* = _____

3. bend - *nd* + *nt* = _____

4. spent - *nt* + *nd* = _____

 As you read the book, look for more words with the letters *nd* or *nt*.
Write the words in your Journal.

✔ Use for Grading

Name _____ **Date** _____

GET READY TO WRITE!

Choose a chapter for your summary. Organize the information on the following chart.

Chapter   What chapter will you summarize? _____

Important Events

_____

_____

_____

What happened first? _____

_____

What happened next? _____

_____

How does the chapter end? _____

_____

✔ Use for Grading

Name _____ **Date** _____

Write a **C**hapter **S**ummary

You've read over your notes and organized your ideas. Now it is time to write your summary paragraph.

Tips

Write your topic sentence with the main idea.

Write sentences describing the important events in sequence.

Tell how it ends.

Use object pronouns such as *him* and *her*.

✔ Use for Grading

Name _____ **Date** _____

Object Pronouns

A Underline each object pronoun in the sentences below.

1. He handed the puppy to me.

2. The trainer asked her to bring the dog inside.

3. Please mail this letter to him right away.

4. Ed picked Fred and me to lead the class today.

5. They enjoyed the dog's tricks and offered him biscuits.

B Write the correct pronoun on the line to complete each sentence.

1. Spot is outside. Who left _____ there? (he, him)

2. The dog carried in the newspaper. She put _____ on the floor. (it, them)

3. Alice has a dog guide. He helped _____ cross the street. (she, her)

4. The trainer asked Glen and _____ to give our dogs the commands. (I, me)

5. I like German shepherds. They like _____, too. (me, her)

6. My friend Pat has three dogs. She feeds _____ carrots. (they, them)

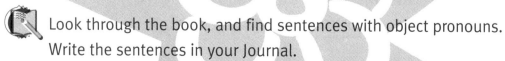

Look through the book, and find sentences with object pronouns. Write the sentences in your Journal.

Name _____ **Date** _____

Consonant Clusters -*nd* and -*nt*

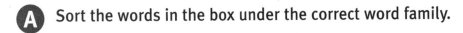

command	want	around	important
depend	amount	ground	went

A Sort the words in the box under the correct word family.

nd

_____

_____

_____

_____

nt

_____

_____

_____

_____

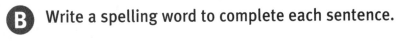

B Write a spelling word to complete each sentence.

1. Can I _____ on you to walk the dog?

2. Jon gave Smokey a _____ to sit.

3. If you _____ to play soccer well, you must practice.

4. Smokey likes to bury her biscuits in the _____ .

5. My family _____ to the beach this weekend.

6. It is _____ to turn off the lights before leaving the house.

7. My friends and I like to walk _____ the lake.

8. Our teacher gave us a large _____ of homework today!

✔ Use for Grading

Name _____ **Date** _____

Silent Letters *kn* and *gn*

The letters *kn* and *gn* stand for the *n* sound in *knight* and *gnat*. Both the *k* and *g* are silent.

A Read the word pairs. Circle the word or words that have silent letters.

1. knew   news
2. nap   gnat
3. sign   sing
4. kind   knee
5. foreign   resign

6. not   gnaw
7. know   known
8. design   pint
9. kit   king
10. knight   night

B Look at the letters below each picture. Put them together with the letters on the knot and the sign to make words with silent letters. Write the words on the lines.

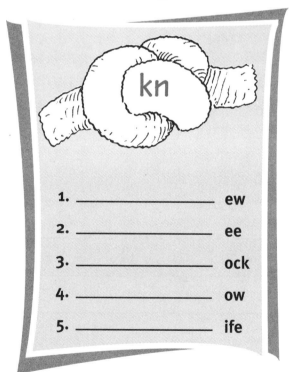

1. _____ ew
2. _____ ee
3. _____ ock
4. _____ ow
5. _____ ife

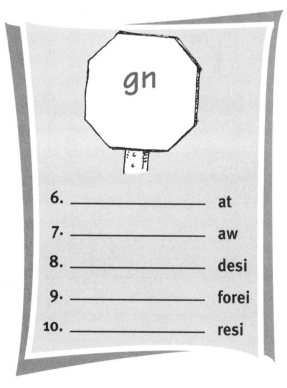

6. _____ at
7. _____ aw
8. _____ desi
9. _____ forei
10. _____ resi

 Choose at least two words with silent letters, and use them to write a funny sentence.

Name _____ **Date** _____

Sound Words

Sound words help make a sentence more descriptive and realistic.

A Read each sentence below. Circle the sound word in each sentence.

1. The open door banged loudly in the wind.

2. The floor creaked as I walked to the window.

3. Mom tells me not to squish my ice cream.

4. The gentle ticking of the clock put me to sleep.

5. I heard clomp, clomp, clomp on the floor above me.

B Write five sentences using at least one of the following sound words in each.

boom	smack	crash
swoosh	zap	splash

1. _____

2. _____

3. _____

4. _____

5. _____

✔ Use for Grading

Name _____ **Date** _____

Reflect and Respond

A Read each question. Circle the best answer.

1. Why did Dorothy Eustis travel from the Alps to Germany?

○ **a.** to find Morris Frank

○ **b.** to find out about dog guides

○ **c.** to start The Seeing Eye school

2. What is the first thing that a dog guide must learn?

○ **a.** to sit at the curb

○ **b.** to get used to a harness

○ **c.** to obey the trainer's commands

3. Why was Buddy so special to Morris Frank?

○ **a.** She found his wallet.

○ **b.** She helped him feel free.

○ **c.** She went with him to get a haircut.

B Read each question. Write your answer on the lines.

1. How long did Buddy serve as Morris's dog guide?

_____

2. What is The Seeing Eye?

_____

_____

What Do You Think? Who do you think was most responsible for making The Seeing Eye school such a success?

Name _____

The Extraordinary Egg

Use the chart below to tell about the main idea and some supporting details of *The Extraordinary Egg*.

Main Idea

Supporting Details

Name _____

Allie's Basketball Dream

Use the chart below to describe Allie from *Allie's Basketball Dream*.

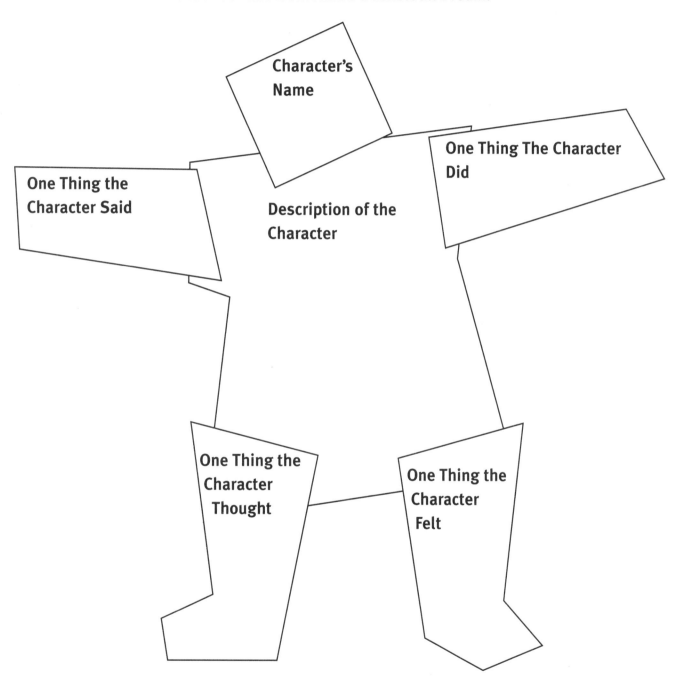

Name _____

The Night I Followed the Dog

Picture clues, text clues, and what you know from your own experience all help you guess what will happen in a story. Use this chart to tell about one of your predictions for *The Night I Followed the Dog.*

Make My Prediction	Clues From the Selection	Clues From What I Know	Confirm or Revise My Prediction

Name _____

Amelia's Road

Using the chart below and the pictures in *Amelia's Road*, write one thing in each box that you learn about Amelia from looking at the pictures in the book.

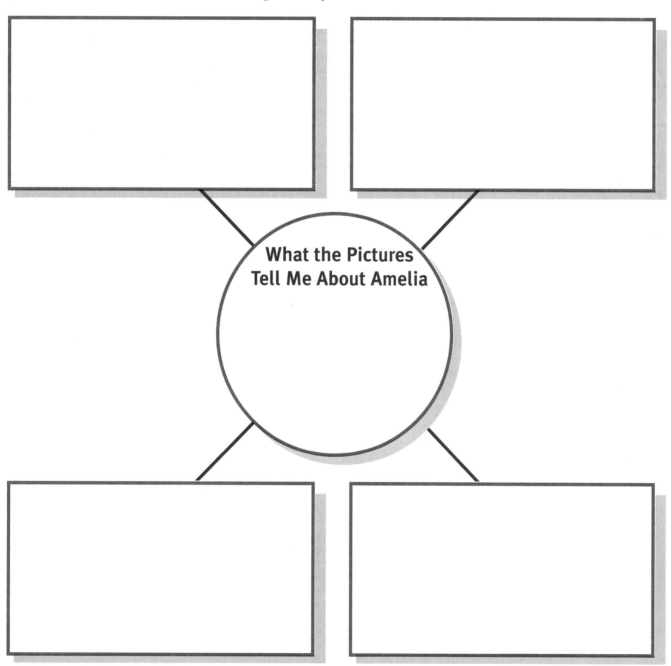

What the Pictures Tell Me About Amelia

Name _____

Cinderella Penguin

Use the Venn diagram below to tell about the similarities and differences between the story *Cinderella Penguin* and the traditional story of *Cinderella*.

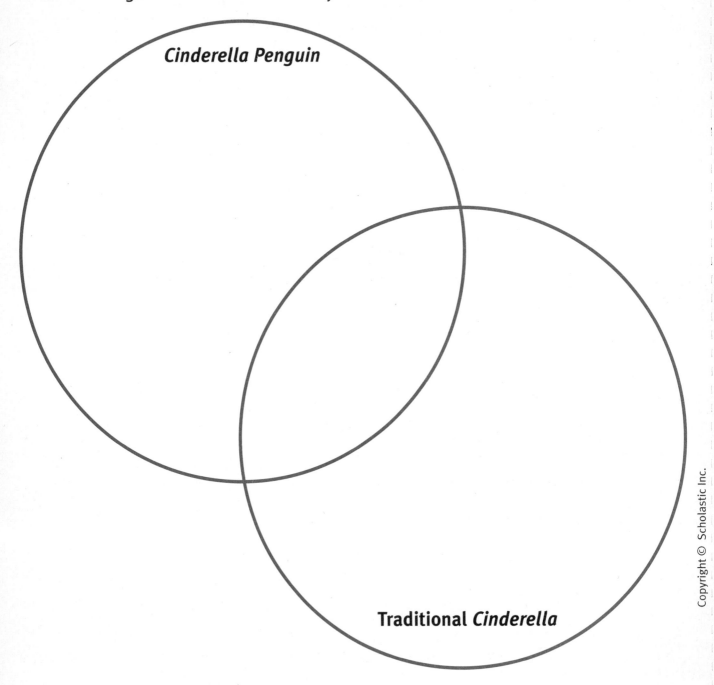

Cinderella Penguin

Traditional *Cinderella*

Name _____

Stargazers

Use the chart below to tell about the main idea and some supporting details of *Stargazers*.

Main Idea

Supporting Details

Name _____

The Birthday Swap

Use the chart on this page to help you tell about the sequence of events in
The Birthday Swap.

First

Next

Then

Last

Name ———————————————————————

Buddy: The First Seeing Eye Dog

Use the chart below to help you summarize information in *Buddy: The First Seeing Eye Dog.* Use your own words in each box.

Important Details

Main Idea

Summary Statement

Glossary

A a

aim(ed) /ām/ *verb*
To point in the direction of a target.

alligator /al i *gā* tər/ *noun*
A large reptile with strong jaws and very sharp teeth.

atmosphere /at məs *fēr*/ *noun*
The layers of air around Earth.

B b

backyard /bak yärd/ *noun*
An open area behind a house.

ball /bôl/ *noun*
A fancy party where there is dancing.

basket(s) /bas kit/ *noun*
1. In basketball, a net shaped like a basket open at the bottom; the goal in basketball. 2. A container made of cane or strips of wood or plastic that often has a handle.

belong /bi lông/ *verb*
To be part of.

bicycle /bī si kəl/ *noun*
A vehicle with two wheels that you ride by pedaling and steering with handlebars.

bird /bûrd/ *noun*
A warm-blooded creature with two legs, wings, feathers, and a beak.

birthday /bûrth *dā*/ *noun*
The day of the year when a person was born.

blind /blīnd/ *adjective*
Having no sense of sight.

bright /brīt/ *adjective*
Giving off a strong or intense light.

C c

cake /kāk/ *noun*
A dessert made of sweet dough covered with icing.

camp /kamp/ *noun*
An outdoor area with tents or cabins where people stay.

candle(s) /kan dl/ *noun*
A thin piece of wax around a string that is burned to give light.

celebrate /sel ə *brāt*/ *verb*
To mark a happy event with special activities.

chase /chās/ *verb*
To run after and try to catch somebody or something.

chew /chōō/ *verb*
To grind food between your teeth.

chores /chôrz/ *noun*
Jobs you have to do around the house.

clear /klēr/ *adjective*
Free of clouds.

commands /kə mandz/ *noun*
Orders or directions.

a	add	ô	order	ŧh	this
ā	ace	ōō	took	zh	vision
â	care	ōō	pool		
ä	palm	u	up		
e	end	û	burn	ə	=
ē	equal	yōō	fuse	a	in *above*
i	it	oi	oil	e	in *sicken*
ī	ice	ou	pout	i	in *possible*
o	odd	ng	ring	o	in *melon*
ō	open	th	thin	u	in *circus*

Glossary

constellation
/ˈkon stə lā shən/ *noun*

A group of stars that forms the outline of a person, animal, or object.

creature /krē chər/ *noun*

A living being, human or animal.

crop (crops) /krop/

1. *noun* A plant that is grown for food. 2. *verb* To cut short.

decoration(s)
/ˈdek ə rā shən/ *noun*

A pretty or colorful object or design used to brighten up something.

discovery /di skuv ə rē/ *noun*

Something that has been found.

doghouse /dog hous/ *noun*

A place where a dog lives.

dream /drēm/ *noun*

A goal or aim.

dribble(d) /drib əl/ *verb*

To move the ball forward by repeated bounces.

fetch /fech/ *verb*

To go get something.

flipper(s) /flip ər/ *noun*

A flat, wide rubber shoe used by people for swimming or diving.

forward /fôr wərd/ *preposition*

Ahead or toward the front.

frog(s) /frog/ *noun*

A small, green or brown animal with webbed feet and long back legs that it uses for jumping.

galaxy /gal ək sē/ *noun*

A group of billions of stars.

gift /gift/ *noun*

Something special you give to someone.

grass /gras/ *noun*

A green plant with long, thin leaves.

guide /gīd/ *noun*

Someone or something that leads or directs.

handle /han dl/ *noun*

Something that is held or turned with the hand.

harvest /här vist/ *noun*

The crops that are collected.

hoop /ho͞op/ *noun*

A circle or ring; the round rim at the top of the net in basketball.

important /im pôr tnt/ *adjective*

Of great meaning or value.

a	add	ô	order	th	this
ā	ace	o͞o	took	zh	vision
â	care	o͞o	pool		
ä	palm	u	up		
e	end	û	burn	ə	=
ē	equal	yo͞o	fuse	a	in *above*
i	it	oi	oil	e	in *sicken*
ī	ice	ou	pout	i	in *possible*
o	odd	ng	ring	o	in *melon*
ō	open	th	thin	u	in *circus*

Glossary

jump /jump/ *verb*

To push off with your legs and feet into the air.

labor (labored) /lā bər/ *verb*

To work hard.

leash (leashes) /lēsh/ *noun*

A chain or strap to hold and control an animal.

matter /mat ər/ *verb*

To be of importance.

maybe /mā bē/ *adverb*

Perhaps.

meadow /med ō/ *noun*

A field of grass.

midnight /mid nīt/ *noun*

12 o'clock at night.

moon /mo͞on/ *noun*

The satellite that moves around Earth once each month and reflects light from the sun.

O o

obey /ō bā/ *verb*

To do what someone tells you, or commands you, to do.

P p

party /pär tē/ *noun*

A gathering of people for a happy purpose.

peach (peaches) /pēch/ *noun*

A soft, sweet fruit with a hard pit and orange skin.

pebble /peb əl/ *noun*

A small, round stone.

poodle /po͞od l/ *noun*

A dog with thick, curly hair.

pool /po͞ol/

1. *noun* A small area of still water. 2. *noun* A game played with different colored balls and long sticks, called cues, the object of which is to hit the balls into pockets on a table. 3. *verb* To contribute to a common fund or effort.

present /prez ənt/ *noun*

1. A gift. 2. Right now.

proudly /proud lē/ *adverb*

In a pleased and self-satisfied manner.

R r

rags /ragz/ *noun*

Old worn-out clothing.

remember /ri mem bər/ *verb*

To recall or to bring back to mind.

S s

shine /shīn/ *verb*

To give off bright light.

shoot /sho͞ot/ *verb*

To throw the ball at the basket.

sky /skī/ *noun*

The arch of air over Earth.

a	add	ô	order	th	this
ā	ace	o͝o	took	zh	vision
â	care	o͞o	pool		
ä	palm	u	up		
e	end	û	burn	ə	=
ē	equal	yo͞o	fuse	a	in *above*
i	it	oi	oil	e	in *sicken*
ī	ice	ou	pout	i	in *possible*
o	odd	ng	ring	o	in *melon*
ō	open	th	thin	u	in *circus*

Glossary

smart /smärt/ *adjective*
1. Clever and quick in thinking. 2. In fashion; elegant.

snack(s) /snak/ *noun*
A small, light meal.

soccer /sok ər/ *noun*
A game played by kicking the ball into a goal.

spell /spel/
1. *noun* An enchanted state caused by magic. 2. *verb* To name the letters of a word.

stargazer /stär *gā* zər/ *noun*
A person who watches the night sky.

stepsister(s) /step *sis* tər/ *noun*
A daughter of your stepfather or stepmother by a former marriage.

stone(s) /stōn/ *noun*
A small piece of rock.

strong /strông/ *adjective*
Powerful; in good health.

surprise /sər **prīz**/ *noun*
Something you don't expect.

tears /tērz/ *noun*
The drops that fall from your eyes when you cry.

think /thingk/ *verb*
To form ideas; to have an idea or opinion.

train /trān/ *verb*
To help a person or an animal learn new skills.

treat (treats) /trēt/ *noun*
Things that you especially enjoy.

twinkle /twing kəl/ *verb*
To shine with quick flashes of light.

wag (wagging) /wag/ *verb*
To move something quickly from side to side.

wand /wond/ *noun*
A thin stick with magical powers.

weed(s) /wēd/ *noun*
A plant that is seen as useless or harmful and growing where it is not wanted.

worker (workers) /wûr kər/ *noun*
A person who does a job.

a	add	ô	order	th	this
ā	ace	o͝o	took	zh	vision
â	care	o͞o	pool		
ä	palm	u	up		
e	end	û	burn	ə	=
ē	equal	yo͞o	fuse	a	in *above*
i	it	oi	oil	e	in *sicken*
ī	ice	ou	pout	i	in *possible*
o	odd	ng	ring	o	in *melon*
ō	open	th	thin	u	in *circus*

accidental/accidental
admire (to)/admirar
allergic/alérgico/a
*animal/animal
announce (to)/anunciar
appear (to)/aparecer
*astronomer/astrónomo
atmosphere/atmósfera
*attention/atención
August/agosto
bicycle/bicicleta
border/borde, frontera
cabin/cabina (of telephone, plane, etc.)
cable/cable
*camera/cámara
*captain/capitán
capture (to)/capturar
celebrate (to)/celebrar
center/centro
ceramic/cerámica
circle/círculo (to circle/rodear)
circular/circular
class/clase
*color/color
commotion/conmoción
completely/completamente
concave/cóncavo/a
constellation/constelación
continue (to)/continuar
*decide (to)/decidir
decoration/decoración, adornos
*delicate/delicado/a
*depend (to)/depender
different/diferente
*direction/dirección
director/director
disappear (to)/desaparecer
discuss/discutir
distance/distancia
*enormous/enorme
enter (to)/entrar
excited/excitado/a
exclaim (to)/exclamar
exotic/exótico/a
extra/extra
*extraordinary/extraordinario/a
*family/familia
*famous/famoso/a
*favorite/favorito/a

*finally/finalmente
firm/firme
*fruit/fruta
funeral/funeral
galaxy/galaxia
garden/huerto, jardín
gas/gas
group/grupo
guide/guía
history/historia
honor/honor
*idea/idea
*important/importante
impressed/impresionado/a
incredible/increíble
inseparable/inseparable
investigate (to)/investigar
*invitation/invitación
*island/isla
labor/labor, tarea
lens/lente
*lesson/lección
*limousine/limusina
locate (to)/localizar
magic/mágico
magnificent/magnífico/a
manner/manera
map/mapa
march/marcha
march (to)/marchar, caminar
marionettes/marionetas
medal/medalla
metal/metal
*million/millón
miniature/miniatura
*minute/minuto
*monument/monumento
much/mucho
musicians/músicos
*natural/natural
necessity/necesidad
notice/noticia
obedience/obediencia
object/objeto
observatory/observatorio
occasion/ocasión
operation/operación
*ordinary/ordinario
palace/palacio
paper/papel

*park/parque
pass/pasar
patience/paciencia
pedal (to)/pedalear
penguin/pingüino
perfect/perfecto/a
perfume/perfume
permanent/permanente
photo/foto
*photograph/fotografía
photographers/fotográfos/as
pioneer/pionero
*planet/planeta
planetarium/planetario
plans/planes
plates/platos
*police/policía
practice/práctica
*practice (to)/practicar
prepare (to)/preparar
present (to)/presentar
pretend/pretender, fingir
*problem/problema
professional/profesional
radio/radio
really/realmente
rest/resto
*reunion/reunión
rock/roca
satin/satén, raso
secret/secreto/a
*sofa/sofá
special/especial
stable/estable
stomach/estómago
study (to)/estudiar
surprise/sorpresa
telescope/telescopio
terrible/terrible
tomato/tomate
totally/totalmente
*tourist/turista
traffic/tráfico
triumphant/triunfante
trumpet/trompeta
tube/tubo
uniform/uniforme
vegetables/vegetales
*visit (to)/visitar
volleyball/voleibol

Copyright © Scholastic Inc.

* Cited in the Teacher's Guide.